EGMONT
We bring stories to life

First published in Great Britain in 2012 by Egmont UK
Limited, 239 Kensington High Street, London W8 6SA

Editor: Catherine Such
Art Editor: Amanda Hartley
Deputy Editor: Julia Millen
Editorial Assistant: Hannah Greenfield
Group Editor: Kate Graham
Group Art Editor: Jeanette Ryall

© 2012 Disney Enterprises, Inc.
The movie *The Princess and the Frog* © 2009 Disney, story
inspired in part by the book *The Frog Princess* by E. D. Baker
© 2002, published by Bloomsbury Publishing, Inc.

ISBN 978 1 4052 6181 4
51260/1
Printed in China

Disney

Princess

This Disney Princess Holiday Annual belongs to

Princess

Write your name here.

Disney PRINCESS
Princess
Holiday Annual

Sticker Play
Use your pretty princess stickers inside.

Princesses ♥ love Animals

The princesses are kind to all creatures. Let's find out about their animal friends.

Woodland Creatures

Aurora and Snow White love spending time in the forest. They have lots of woodland friends, including squirrels, rabbits and deer.

Under the Sea

Ariel has lots of friends at the bottom of the ocean. Her best friend is Flounder, a yellow and blue fish.

Nice Mice

Cinderella's mouse friends help her to sew. Together they make beautiful ball gowns that are fit for a princess.

Funny Friend

Rapunzel's best friend is Pascal the chameleon. He is very funny and knows how to make Rapunzel smile.

9

Underwater Changes

Ariel's playing with her dolphin friends. Can you spot five differences in picture b?

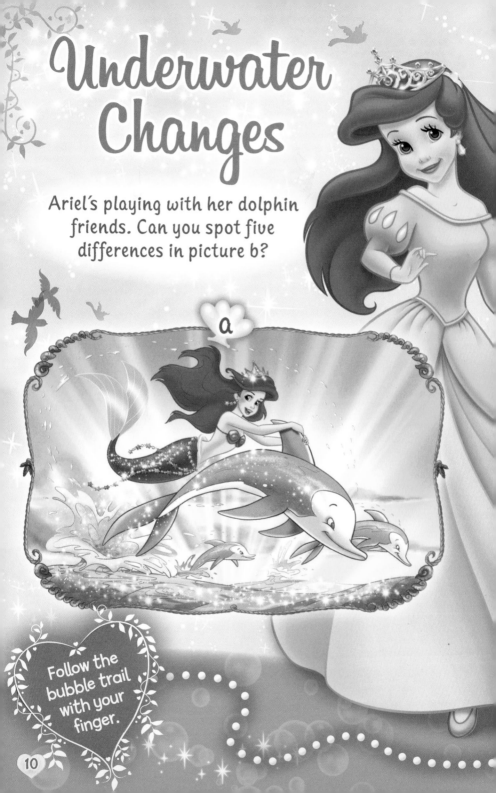

a

Follow the bubble trail with your finger.

Cinderella's

It was a very special day at the palace. A royal pet show was taking place and all the local pets were invited.

Puppy

2 Cinderella smiled as she greeted
the guests, but she felt sad.
Cinderella wished she had her
own pet to enter in the show.

3 Just then, Cinderella heard a noise coming from outside. When she went to look, she found a stray puppy.

4 As Cinderella ran a bath for the puppy, she had an idea. "I could enter you in the pet show!" The puppy barked happily.

5 The judges loved the puppy and she was awarded first place. Cinderella was delighted as she received her trophy.

6 Just then, the puppy spotted her own puppy prince! "Now we'll all live happily ever after," laughed Cinderella.

The End

Sticker Play Add a puppy sticker when you have finished reading the story.

Animal Shadows

Can you help Rapunzel match Pascal
and Maximus to their correct shadows?

Answers on page 58.

19

Princesses ♥ love Dressing-up

Royal wardrobes are full of beautiful clothes and pretty accessories. Let's find out more ...

Sparkling Jewels

Sequins and jewels make the princesses' gowns sparkle. Aurora adores diamonds and Snow White loves rubies.

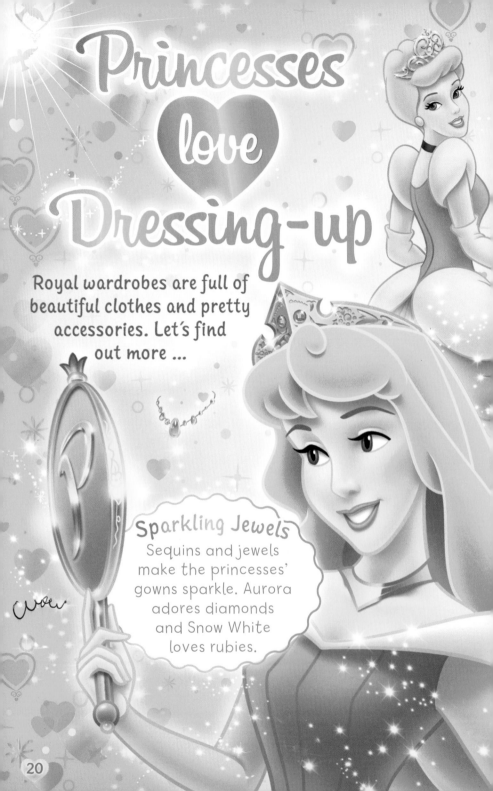

Beautiful Ball Gowns

The princesses all have a favourite outfit. Belle often wears her pretty yellow dress and Cinderella cherishes her blue ball gown.

Helping Hands

The Wardrobe creates pretty outfits for Belle, and Cinderella's bird friends help her to dress every morning.

Finishing Touch

A royal outfit wouldn't be complete without some pretty jewellery. Princesses love tiaras, necklaces and earrings.

Tiana has lost her necklace. Can you find it on these pages?

21

Beautiful Belle

Belle is getting ready for a ball. Guide her through the maze, collecting her accessories on the way.

Start

Finish

Answer on page 58.

Sticker Play

Add a Belle sticker when you have finished.

Tiara Time

Tiana has lots of sparkling tiaras. Can you draw lines to match them into pairs?

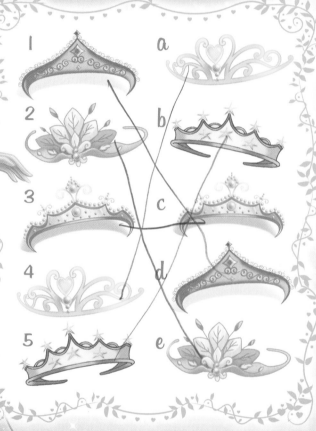

1
2
3
4
5

a
b
c
d
e

Answers on page 58.

Add a pretty pattern to Cinderella's beautiful ball gown.

Sticker Play
Use your jewel stickers to decorate Cinderella's dress.

25

Flower Dress

Look for the stickers below on your sticker sheet and use them to complete the story.

One day was

invited to a sea ball.

She was very excited

but she didn't have a

 to wear. "What can

I do?" asked Luckily, he had an

idea 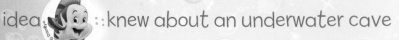 knew about an underwater cave

that was full of pretty 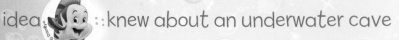 . He told

Dress

Ariel

Sea-flowers

Flounder

Necklace

to follow him. Once there, the friends

picked a huge bunch, then used the

to decorate an old It looked

wonderful! added a pretty

and tiara, and headed off to the sea

ball. "You'll be the best-dressed mermaid

there!" told his friend, excitedly.

The little mermaid smiled happily.

The End

Sticker Play

Pretty Princesses

Follow the trails to match each princess to her favourite accessory.

Draw your favourite accessory in the space below.

mermaid

Answers on page 58.

Royal Wardrobe

What's your princess style?
Choose your favourite dress,
shoes and tiara to find out!

Sticker Play

Mostly Pink

You are just like Aurora! You love pretty pinks and like to dress up every single day.

Look at the colour of the circles around your stickers to work out your answer!

Mostly Blue

Your wardrobe looks like Cinderella's! You love beautiful dresses and sparkling jewellery.

Add some colour to this cheeky mouse.

Mostly Purple

You and Ariel share the same style! You like wearing comfy clothes with a few pretty accessories.

If you chose one of each colour, you're lucky enough to have a mixture of princess styles!

Princesses ♥ love Princes

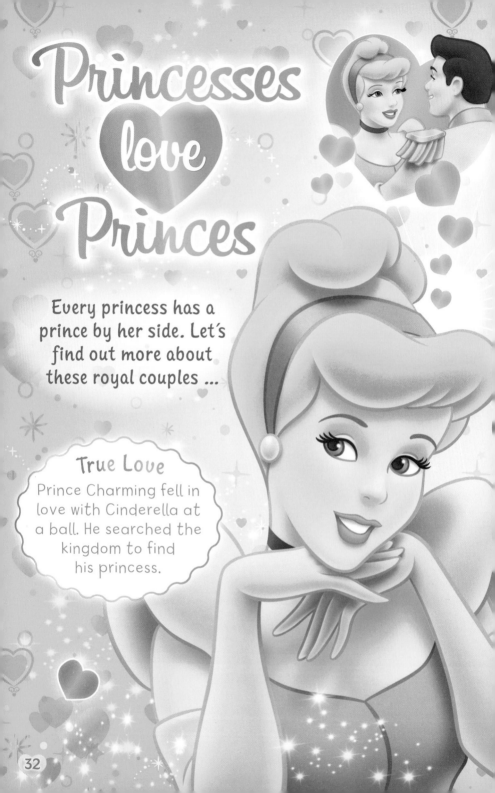

Every princess has a prince by her side. Let's find out more about these royal couples ...

True Love

Prince Charming fell in love with Cinderella at a ball. He searched the kingdom to find his princess.

Perfect Prince

Snow White always dreamed of meeting a handsome prince. One day, her wish came true!

Gentle Giant

Belle's prince, the Beast, may look scary but Belle has taught him how to be kind and gentle.

How many blue hearts can you count on these pages?

2

Magical Moment

Prince Naveen and Tiana fell in love as frogs. When they were married, the spell was magically broken.

Answer on page 58.

Royal Couples

Can you find the names of these princes and princesses in the wordsearch?

N	A	V	A	R	I	G	H	U	P
E	R	F	L	Y	N	N	A	T	R
B	I	R	T	R	R	M	L	I	I
E	R	I	C	A	I	B	I	A	N
A	E	G	A	P	Y	O	A	N	C
R	U	A	I	U	I	J	R	A	E
I	F	R	K	N	A	V	E	E	N
N	E	I	O	Z	L	E	R	I	S
C	Q	E	R	E	O	T	D	E	U
Z	S	L	A	U	R	V	E	Y	T

Sticker Play
Add a sticker as you find each name.

RAPUNZEL

ARIEL

TIANA

FLYNN

ERIC

NAVEEN

34

Answers on page 59.

Belle is dancing
with the Beast.
Add some romantic
colours to
this picture.

Time for Love

Aurora had a busy day planned, full of royal engagements. She hardly had time to see her prince.

2 By the end of the day, Aurora was feeling tired, but she was looking forward to spending time with Prince Phillip.

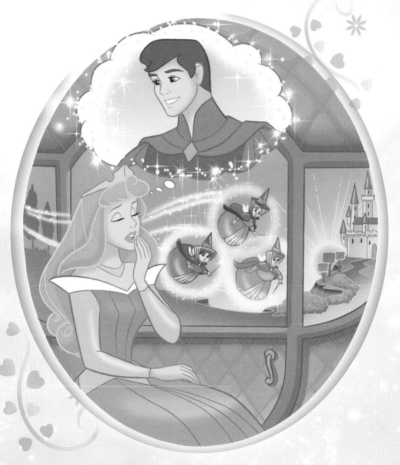

3 Back at the palace, lots
of people were waiting for
Aurora. The fairies decided
to help the royal couple.

4 "You need some time to yourselves," the fairies said, sprinkling sleeping powder on everyone in the kingdom.

5 Aurora and the prince had a whole hour before the spell wore off. They took a balloon ride together.

6 Back on the ground, the prince took Aurora's hand. "Every hour is magical when I'm with you," he said.

The End

Sticker Play

Add a star sticker when you have finished reading the story.

Which Prince?

Use the clues below to work out which
prince has a present for his princess.

The Beast

Prince Charming

He is wearing a cape.

He has brown eyes.

He has a flower on his belt.

The Prince

Prince Naveen

Answer on page 59.

Mirror Message

Rapunzel has received a love letter from Flynn. Hold this page up to a mirror to reveal what it says.

Our love will last forever.

Sticker Play
Use a heart sticker to complete the sequence.

Which colour heart comes next in this sequence?

43

Answers on page 59.

Princesses ♥love♥ Parties

Princesses enjoy celebrating special occasions. Read on to find out more about princess parties ...

Tea Time

Snow White enjoys having tea parties with the Dwarfs. She always bakes their favourite cakes.

Which present is the odd one out?

a b c

Beautiful Balls

Cinderella likes to host balls at the palace. It reminds her of meeting Prince Charming for the first time.

Floating Lights

When Rapunzel returned to the King and Queen, they had a big party and released lanterns into the sky.

Magical Music

Ariel loves the sound of lively music. There's always a band playing at her exciting underwater parties.

Add some colour to the musical notes.

45

Answer on page 59.

Shadow Dance

Can you draw lines to match the
dancing princesses to their shadows?

Sticker Play

Add a ballet shoe sticker when you have finished.

© Disney

47

Answers on page 59.

Party Time

Tiana is planning a party for her friends. Can you count how many of each party item she has?

Write the numbers in the boxes.

a   b   c   d   e

 1   2   4   3   1

Answers on page 59.

Tiana and Louis are partying in the bayou. Use your brightest pens to finish this picture.

A Special Surprise

Rapunzel wanted to throw a surprise
party for Pascal. She asked her
friend, Princess .....Lana.........
to help. "I'd love to!" Princess
.......Laha............ cried.

First, they decorated the room.
Princess .....Laha............
was very good at blowing
up balloons.

Next, they baked
some cakes. Princess
.....Lana............ made a
yummy strawberry sponge.

Sticker Play
Add a Rapunzel sticker when you've finished reading your story.

Then they planned some party games. Princess ....Lana........ had lots of fun ideas.

Finally, the guests arrived and Rapunzel went to find Pascal.

As they came in to the room, Princess ....Lana........ and the excited guests shouted "Surprise!" Pascal scurried around with delight.

Rapunzel said thank you to Princess ....Lana........ for all her help.

"That's what friends are for," replied Princess ....Lana.........

The End

51

Jigsaw Puzzle

Cinderella is dancing at a garden ball. Use your jigsaw stickers to finish the picture.

Sticker Play

Add jigsaw stickers to complete the scene.

Which of these pictures is the odd one out?

Answer on page 59.

Party Cakes

Rapunzel has baked some delicious cakes. Can you help her complete these activities?

a

b

Draw lines to match the cupcakes into pairs.

c

d

e

Use your prettiest pens to decorate this cake.

f

g

h

Answers on page 59.

Add some bright colours to this picture of Rapunzel getting ready for a princess party.

Princess loves

Write your name here.

The princesses would like to know what you love. Fill in these pages all about yourself.

Animals
Write the name of your favourite animal below.

Princes
Draw your perfect prince here.

princes
Eric

Parties

Tick which type of party you like best.

Sleepover ☐

Disco ☐

Dressing-up

Draw your favourite outfit here.

Sticker Play

Use your heart and jewel stickers to decorate your outfit.

Answers

Pages 10-11
Underwater Changes

Pages 18-19
Animal Shadows
1 - a, 2 - b.

Pages 22-23
Beautiful Belle

Page 24
Tiara Time
1 and d, 2 and e, 3 and c, 4 and a, 5 and b.

Pages 28-29
Pretty Princesses
Belle - fan, Tiana - pendant, Aurora - tiara.

Pages 32-33
Princesses l♥ve Princes
3 blue hearts.

Page 34
Royal Couples

Page 42
Which Prince?
Prince Naveen.

Page 43
Mirror Message
Our love will last forever.
A blue heart comes next.

Pages 44-45
Princesses love Parties
Present b.

Pages 46-47
Shadow Dance
1 - d, 2 - c, 3 - a, 4 - b.

Page 48
Party Time
a - 1, b - 2, c - 4, d - 3, e - 1.

Pages 52-53
Jigsaw Puzzle
c is the odd one out.

Page 54
Party Cakes
a and d, b and e, c and g, f and h.

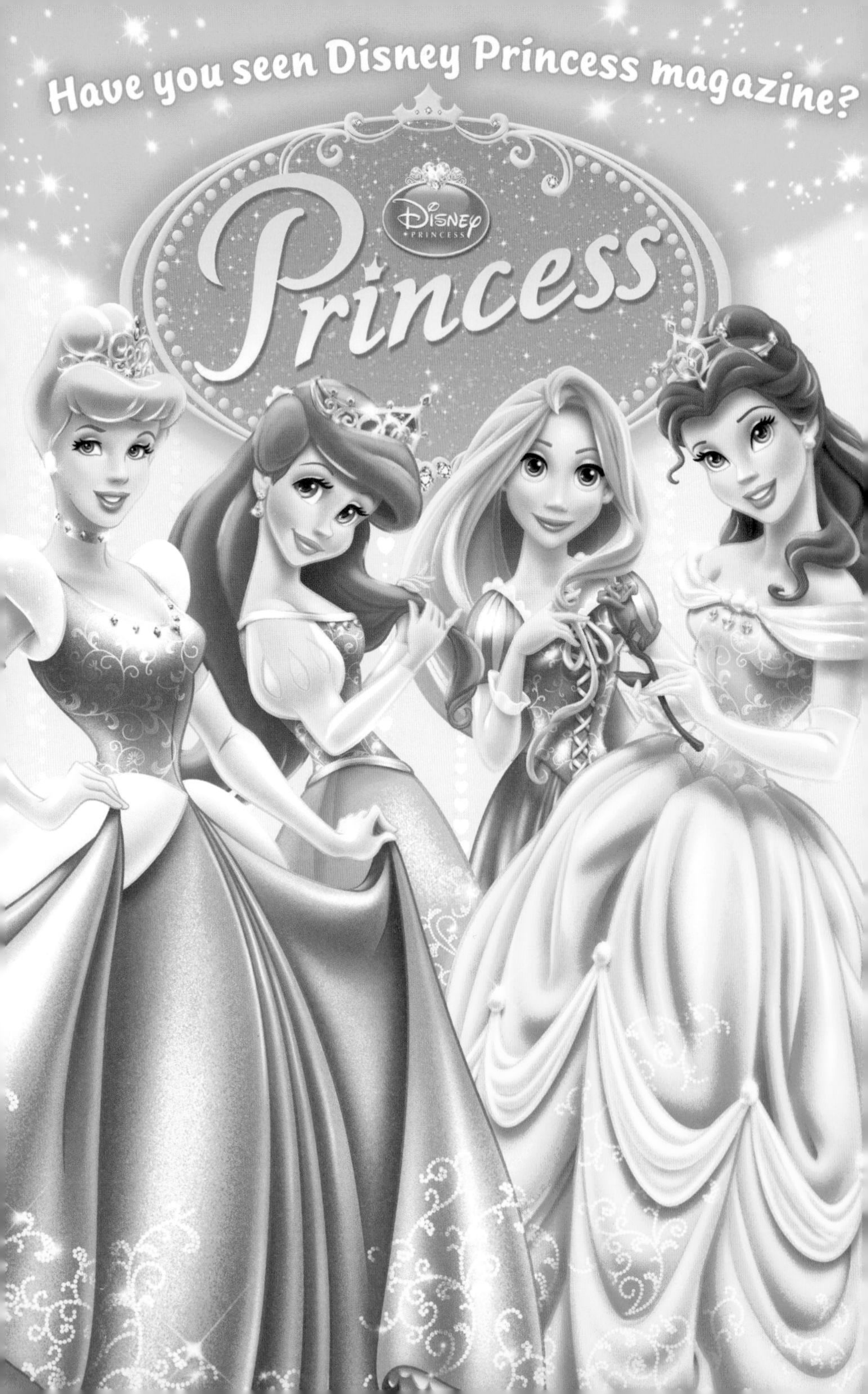
Have you seen Disney Princess magazine?
Disney
PRINCESS
Princess